KEEP
CALM
AND
COLOUR
ON

HUCK &
PUCKER

Daydreaming with pencil and paper is
a respectable form of meditation.

John Howe

Happy is he who still loves something
he loved in the nursery.

G. K. Chesterton

In times of stress drawing is a
way of relieving tension.

Gene Black

Get out of your head and get into your
heart. Think less, feel more.

Osho

Put your heart, mind, and soul into even your
smallest acts. This is the secret of success.

Sivananda Saraswati

Man needs colour to live; it's just as necessary an element as fire and water.

Fernand Léger

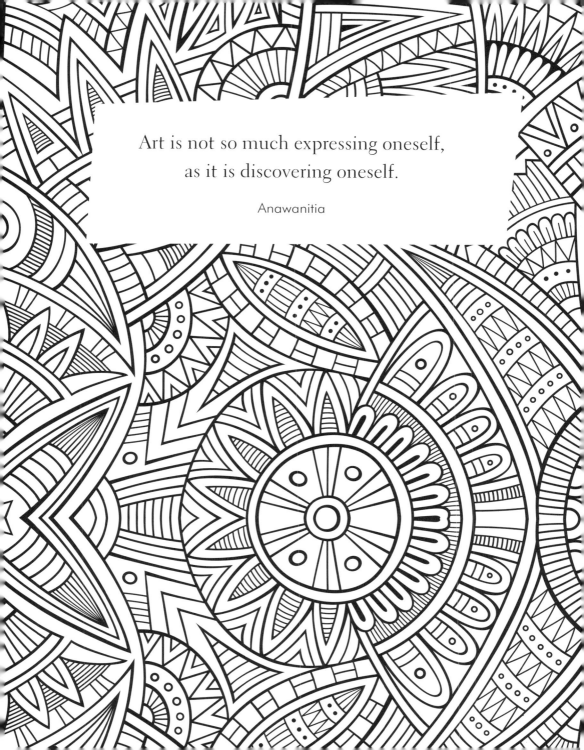

Art is not so much expressing oneself,
as it is discovering oneself.

Anawanitia

The most powerful weapon on earth
is the human soul on fire.

Ferdinand Foch

Let go of your mind and
then be mindful.

Rumi

To draw, you must close your eyes and sing.

Pablo Picasso

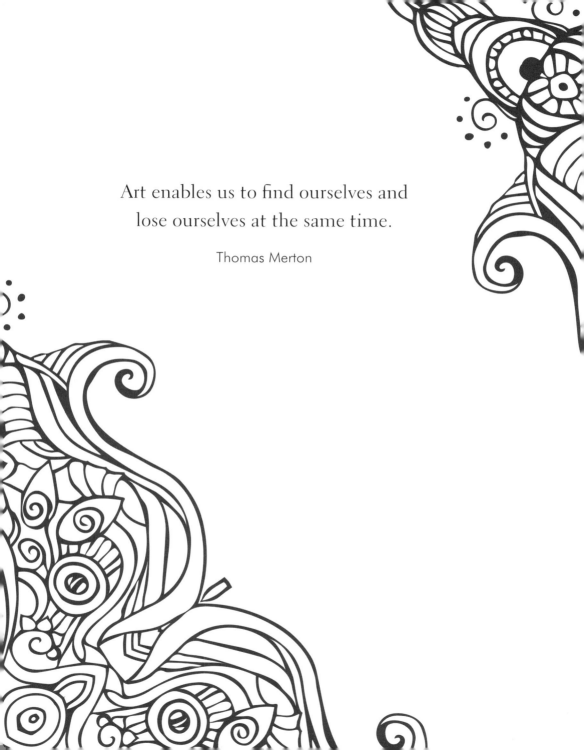

Art enables us to find ourselves and
lose ourselves at the same time.

Thomas Merton

Art holds out the promise of inner wholeness.

Alain de Botton

Red is passion-lit, orange is flowerageous,
yellow is suntastic, pink is lipsensual, green is
lifebursting, blue is skyful, purple is berrydancing.

Terri Guillemets

If you want to be creative, stay in part a child.

Jean Piaget

No art comes from the conscious mind.

Steve Martin

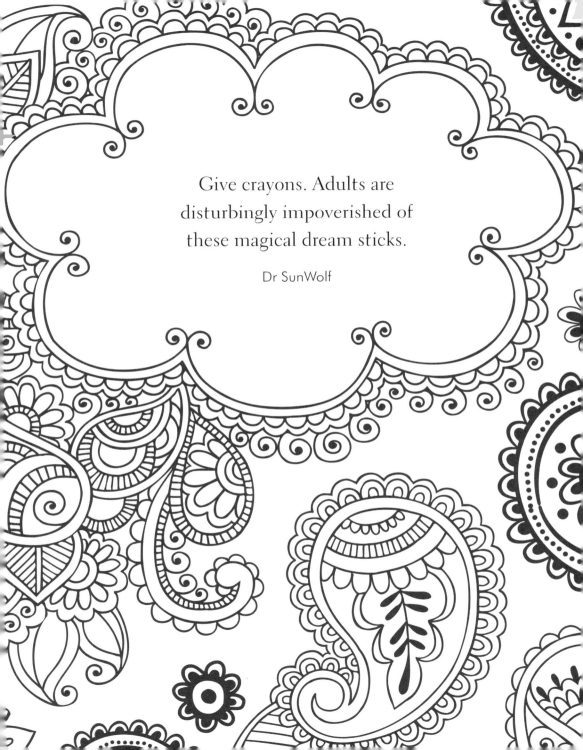

Give crayons. Adults are
disturbingly impoverished of
these magical dream sticks.

Dr SunWolf

One eye sees, the other feels.

Paul Klee

All the other colours are just colours, but purple seems to have a soul – when you look at it, it's looking back at you.

Uniek Swain

I love colour. I feel it inside
me. It gives me a buzz.

Damien Hirst

I am a believer that colour affects people's moods.

Lilly Pulitzer

Be happy in the moment, that's enough.
Each moment is all we need, not more.

Mother Teresa

Each colour lives by its mysterious life.

Wassily Kandinsky

Art is, for me, the process of
trying to wake up the soul.

Bill Viola

Who looks outside, dreams;
who looks inside, awakes.

Carl Jung

Happiness arises in a state of
peace, not of tumult.

Ann Radcliffe

Colours, like features, follow the
changes of the emotions.

Pablo Picasso

Art is therapy for my soul.

Reno

They're only crayons. You didn't fear them
in kindergarten, why fear them now?

Hugh MacLeod

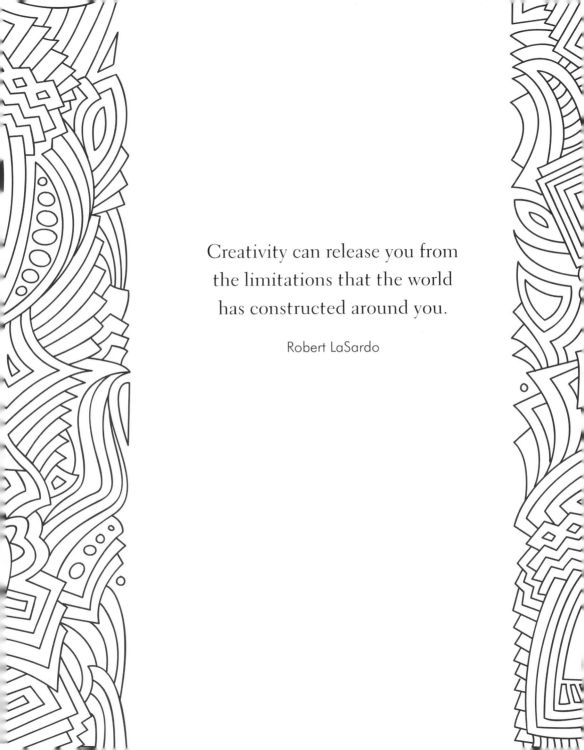

Creativity can release you from
the limitations that the world
has constructed around you.

Robert LaSardo

I cannot pretend to be impartial
about the colours. I rejoice with the
brilliant ones, and am genuinely
sorry for the poor browns.

Winston Churchill

Man needs spiritual
expression and nourishing.

Fernando Botero

The colours live a remarkable
life of their own after they have
been applied to the canvas.

Edvard Munch

I sometimes think there is nothing
so delightful as drawing.

Vincent Van Gogh

The purest and most thoughtful minds
are those which love colour the most.

John Ruskin

An artist cannot fail; it is
a success to be one.

Charles Horton Cooley

For fast-acting relief, try slowing down.

Lily Tomlin

Man is most nearly himself
when he achieves the seriousness
of a child at play.

Heraclitus

Colours are the smiles of nature.

Leigh Hunt

I found I could say things with colour
and shapes that I couldn't say any other
way – things I had no words for.

Georgia O'Keeffe

Art washes from the soul the dust of everyday life.

Pablo Picasso

Everything you do can be done
better from a place of relaxation.

Stephen C. Paul

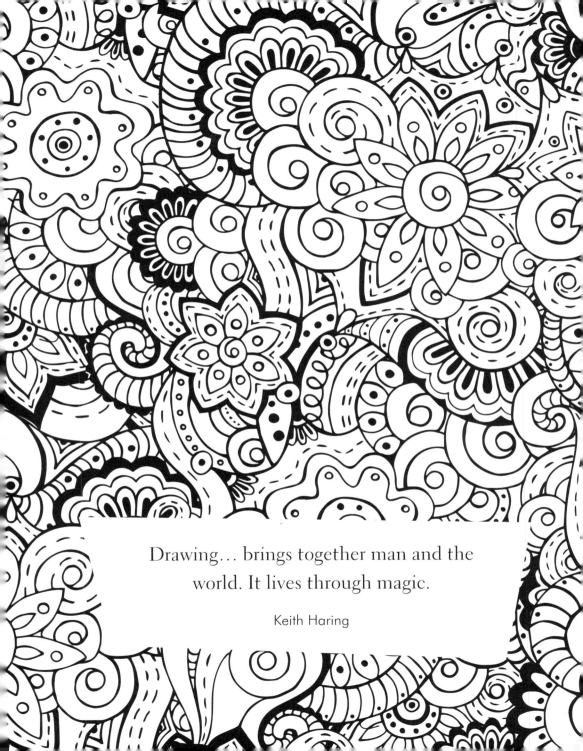

Drawing… brings together man and the world. It lives through magic.

Keith Haring

In every real man a child is
hidden that wants to play.

Friedrich Nietzsche

Colour is the fruit of life.

Guillaume Apollinaire

Colour is my day-long
obsession, joy and torment.

Claude Monet

The great man is he who does
not lose his child-heart.

Mencius

The pursuit, even of the best things,
ought to be calm and tranquil.

Cicero

If you're interested in finding out
more about our products, find us on
Facebook at **HuckAndPucker** and
follow us on Twitter at **@HuckandPucker**.

www.huckandpucker.com

Huck & Pucker
Huck Towers
46 West Street
Chichester
West Sussex
PO19 1RP
UK

www.huckandpucker.com

Printed and bound in the Czech Republic

ISBN: 978-1-909865-12-9

Substantial discounts on bulk quantities of Huck & Pucker books are available to corporations, professional associations and other organisations. For details contact Nicky Douglas by telephone: +44 (0) 1243 756902, fax: +44 (0) 1243 786300 or email: nicky@summersdale.com.